land

● Helsinki

● Moscow

● Berlin

Istanbul

Cairo ●

os

Nairobi ●

● Bejing

Tokyo

● New Delhi

● Manila

Jakarta ●

Darwin ●

Cape Town

Sydney ●

Timezones

+1   +2   +3   +4   +5   +6   +7   +8   +9   +10   +11   +12

RAIMO SUIKKARI

Finland
knows

PHOTOGRAPHS

Aker Finnyards 52,
Bio Turku Oy 56, 57
DAPSS/ Civil Aviation Administration 25
Desing Pertti Palmroth/Hamken Oy 54, 55
Elektro Metalli Oy 80 (top)
Envisat 23
Esa 22
Finnair 38
Heinonen Unto 51
Heureka 36 (bottom) ja 37
KCI Konecranes Oy 43
Karppinen Tiina/Ideamainos Oy 68, 69
Kolho Matti 64
Lahtinen Taina/FIMOT/ABB 51
Korhonen Tanja 84
Leppänen Jyrki/Naps Systems Oy 30
Lappalainen Tommi 88
Lindström Ella 75 (top)
Metorex International Oy 24 /top)
Kajaanin Teknologiakeskus Oy 81 (top)
Niemelä Voitto 44, 45
Nokia Oy 8, 32, 33
Okkonen Ilpo78
Oulun kaupunki 80, 81 (bottom)
Oy SaunaMare Ltd 72, 73
Potkonen Pentti 75 (centre and bottom)
Suikkari Raimo, all other pictures
Technopolis Oy 82
Teknilinen korkeakoulu Helsinki 26, 27
Tikka Martti/PVK 10
Turo Teilor Oy 70, 71
Valmela Tarmo 66, 67
Villanen Timo 74
Vänskä-Kauhanen Tarja 58 (bottom)
VTT 20, 22
Wärtsilä Oyj 50

REFERENCES

Statistics Finland 5, 6, 7, 13, 17, 49, 65, 79, 87
Gounty governments 12, 13, 16, 17, 48, 49, 64, 65, 78, 79, 86, 87
University of Helsinki 18
Polytechnics in Finland 6
The companies mentioned in the book.

Planning and implementation:
Raimo Suikkari
© Copyright: Raimo Suikkari/RKS Tietopalvelu Oy
Layout: Iiris Illukka
Translation: Marianne Lindahl
Publisher: RKS Tietopalvelu Oy
Printed by Karisto Oy, Hämeenlinna 2004
Paper: Galerie Art Gloss 150 g
1st Edition
ISBN 952-5308-32-4 (sid.)
ISBN 952-5308-34-0 (nid.)

This book has been published without exterior funds or grants.

Finland knows

During the last decades, Finnish technology and know-how have reached a top position in the world. In 2003, Finland was ranked number one in a prestigious international global competitiveness survey.

The hard work of previous generations in a predominantly agrarian society has created a solid ground for a spectacular development in the fields of technology, science and industry. Outstanding achievements in space and information technology, solar energy utilization, physics, ship building and paper industry represent some of many recent Finnish success stories.

The high standard of Finnish know-how is a result of flexible cooperation between communities, universities, polytechnics and the business world. This cooperation has lead to many state-of-the-art innovations and inventions. The achievements mentioned in this book are just some examples of Finnish know-how, randomly selected to represent top performances in their respective fields.

I wish to express my gratitude to the companies, communities and private persons who have provided me with valuable assistance and information for this book.

RAIMO SUIKKARI

Finland-info

Population: 5 219 732 on 31.12.2003
Population density: 17 inhabitants/km²,
province of Uusimaa: 224,6 inhabitants/km²,
Lapland: 2,0 inhabitants/km².
Average annual population growth: 0,2%
Life expectancy: 74,9 (men), 81,5 (women)
Government: Republic
Languages: Finnish, Swedish (6%), Sami in the Sami regions, English is the first foreign language taught in schools.
Religions: Evangelic-Lutheran 4 406 594, Greek Orthodox 56 689

Location: Between 60 and 70 Northern Latitude
Longest distance from North to South: 1157 km, and from east to West 541 km.
Time: + 2 hours to GMT
Average temperature: Helsinki, February -5 degrees C, July + 17 degrees C; Sodankylä (Lapland): January -14 degrees C, July + 14 degrees C
National day: 6.12. (Independence day)
Monetary unit: Euro (1 Euro = 100 cents)
GNP 27512€ per capita (2003)

| Åland | Southern Finland | Western Finland | Eastern Finland | Oulu | Lapland |

Number of inhabitants in the biggest cities 31.12.2003:
Helsinki 559 330, Espoo 224 231,
Tampere 200 966, Vantaa 184 039,
Turku 175 059, Oulu 125 928 ,
Lahti 98 253, Kuopio 88 250
Jyväskylä 84 409, Pori 76 189,
Lappeenranta 58 897, Vaasa 56 953,
Kotka 54 618, Joensuu 52 659,
Hämeenlinna 46 909, Mikkeli 46 511,
Porvoo 46 217 and Hyvinkää 43 169.

The County of Lapland

The County of Oulu

The County of Eastern Finland

The County of Western Finland

The County of Southern Finland

The Province of the Åland Islands

Helsinki: University of Helsinki, Helsinki School of Economics and Business Administration, Academy of Fine Arts, The Finnish National Defence Academy, Swedish School of Economics and Business Administration, Swedish School of Social Science, University of Helsinki, Sibelius Academy, University of Art and Design, Helsinki Theatre Academy Finland, Espoo: Technical University of Helsinki, Hämeenlinna: Tampere University, Hämeenlinna Vocational Teacher Education College, Joensuu: Joensuu University, Jyväskylä: Jyväskylä University, Kajaani: Oulu University, Kajaani Vocational Teacher Education College, Kouvola: Helsinki University, Department of Translation Studies at Kouvola, Kuopio: Kuopio University, Lahti: Helsinki University, Lappeenranta: Lappeenranta Technical University, Mikkeli: Helsinki School of Economics and Business Administration, Oulu: Oulu University, Pori: Tampere Technical University, Turku University, Rauma: Turku University Department for Teacher Education, Rovaniemi:University of Lapland, Savonlinna: Joensuu University Department of International Communication, Savonlinna Vocational Teacher Education College, Tampere: Tampere University, Tampere Technical University, Turku: Turku University, Åbo Akademi University (Swedish)Turku School of Economics and Business Administration, Vaasa: Vaasa University, Åbo Akademi Teacher Education Department (Swedish) Swedish School of Economics and Business Administration

POLYTECHNICS

Arcada - Swedish Polytechnic of Nyland, Central Ostrobothnia Polytechnic, Diaconia Institute of Higher Education in Finland, Espoo-Vantaa Institute of Technology, Haaga Institute Polytechnic, Helsinki Business Polytechnic, Helsinki Polytechnic, Humanities Polytechnic Institute of Studies of Human Relations and Activities, Häme Polytechnic, Jyväskylä Polytechnic, Kajaani Polytechnic, Kemi-Tornio Polytechnic, Kymenlaakso Polytechnic, Lahti Polytechnic, Laurea Polytechnic, Mikkeli Polytechnic, North Carelia Polytechnic, North Savo Polytechnic, Oulu Polytechnic, Pirkanmaa Polytechnic, Rovaniemi Polytechnic, Satakunta Polytechnic, Seinäjoki Polytechnic, South Carelia Polytechnic, Swedish Polytechnic, Finland, Sydväst Polytechnic, Tampere Polytechnic, Turku Polytechnic, Vaasa Polytechnic, Other Finnish Polytechnics: Insitute of Higher Education of the Province of Åland and the Police College of Finland governed by the Ministry of Internal Affairs.

Finland's most important trading partners for high-tech products 2002

Export countries	Million €	%	Import countries	Million €	%
Great Britain	1 397,6	14,4	USA	1 203,7	21,1
Germany	707,9	7,3	Germany	661,1	11,6
France	623,7	6,4	Japan	545,1	9,6
USA	607,7	6,3	Great Britain	466,3	8,2
Russia	590,7	6,1	China	449,5	7,9
United Arab Emir.	487,8	5,0	Sweden	265,2	4,7
Italy	427,1	4,4	Estonia	208,2	3,7
Sweden	337,9	3,5	Ireland	195,6	3,4
China	316,5	3,3	Netherlands	163,9	2,9
Switzerland	269,3	2,8	Malaysia	150,2	2.6
Netherlands	269,0	2,8	Taiwan	137,3	2,4
Saudi-Arabia	237,1	2,4	South Korea	125,1	2,2
Japan	231,0	2,4	France	124,2	2,2
Ireland	198,5	2,0	Denmark	115,0	2,0
Thailand	183,6	1,9	Switzerland	82,5	1,5
Hong Kong	181,3	1,9	Singapore	81,4	1,4
Greece	179,1	1,8	Italy	74,6	1,3
Poland	174,1	1,8	Hungary	74,5	1.3
Spain	171,9	1,8	Czech Republic	62,3	1,1
Denmark	143,9	1,5	Belgium	58,0	1,0
Total	7 735,9	79,6		5 246,5	92,1
Other countries	1 977,3	20,4		449,5	7,9
Total exports	9 713,2	100,0	Total imports	5 696,0	100,0

100 LARGEST FINNISH COMPANIES (BY TURNOVER IN MAY 2003)

1. Nokia
2. Stora Enso
3. Nordea Bank Finland
4. Fortum
5. UPM-Kymmene
6. Metsäliitto
7. Kesko
8. Outokumpu
9. Metso
10. Kone
11. Tamro
12. Varma-Sampo
13. Ilmarinen
14. SOK
15. Rautaruukki
16. Sampo
17. Kemira
18. Wärtsilä
19. Sanoma-Wsoy
20. Sonera
21. Huhtamäki
22. Elcoteq Network
23. Ahlstrom
24. YIT-Yhtymä
25. Inex
26. Finnair
27. Orion
28. Valio
29. Elisa
30. ABB-Yhtiöt
31. Wihuri
32. Myllykoski
33. Nordea Life Insurance
34. Stockmann
35. Eläke-Tapiola
36. Tieto-Enator
37. Lemminkäinen
38. Pohjola
39. Suomi
40. Tradeka
41. Skanska
42. VR-Yhtymä
43. Uponor
44. Instrumentarium
45. Suomen Posti
46. Amer
47. Alko
48. Veikkaus
49. Onvest
50. Dynea
51. If Indemnity Insurance
52. OMG Finland
53. Kvaerner Masa-Yards
54. Teboil

54. Teboil
55. Sanitec
56. Hartwall
57. Eläke-Fennia
58. Osuuspankkikeskus
59. Raisio Yhtymä
60. Fazer
61. NCC Finland
62. Fiskars
63. KCI Konecranes
64. Atria
65. Finnlines
66. Tuko Logistics
67. Veho
68. Pohjolan Voima
69. Shell
70. HK Ruokatalo
71. Rettig
72. HOK73. Suomen Spar
74. Aurum Henkivakuutus
75. Vahinko-Tapiola
76. Volvo Auto
77. Gasum
78. Raha-automaattiyhdistys
79. Toyota Motor
80. Consolis
81. Borealis Polymer
82. GNT Finland
83. Silja
84. Shenker East
85. Alma Media
86. Nokian Renkaat
87. Kuusakoski
88. Foster Wheeler Energia
89. Veritas
90. Vapo
91. Henki-Tapiola
92. Suomen Petrooli
93. Siemens
94. Jaakko Pöyry
95. KWH-Yhtymä
96. Viking Line
97. Metro-Auto
98. Hewlett-Packard
99. Elanto
100. Starkki

Finnish Architecture

The Nokia-house in Keilaniemi, Espoo, was designed by Pekka Helin and finished in 1997. The building has been awarded a prestigious prize for its stylish and original energy-saving glass façade. The interior design, favouring natural materials, is by Iiris Ulin.

During the last few years, many office buildings have been built in the vicinity of the Nokia-house, e.g. the offices of Fortum Oyj, designed by architects Castrén-Jauhiainen-Nuuttila (centre),

Iso Paja (The Big Workshop) is a part of the Finnish Broadcasting Company (YLE) complex in Pasila. It is designed by Ilmo Valjakka, and was finished in 1993.

Finnish Peacekeeping Expertise

UN peacekeeping has been the most visible part of the international activity of the Finnish military establishment. Today Finland also participates in peacekeeping missions lead by other security organizations in a number of operations all over the world. Over the past fifty years, more than 43 000 men and women have served in different peacekeeping activities. Finnish peacekeepers are known for their high morale and outstanding skills.

Creating order in the ranks at Säkylä garrison.

Inspection of the crew of a vehicle arriving at the Finnish Camp, FinCamp.

YKSRJEE stands for Finnish UN Peace keeping unit in Ethiopia.

Finnish intelligence unit on a mission in Macedonia.

Military band playing at the Senaatintori square in Helsinki. >

Know-how in the Province of the Åland Islands.

Shipping, agriculture, fishing and tourism are Åland's main sources of living.
Industries are on a relatively small scale, the number of small-scale enterprises being
1800. The main industries involve processing of fish and agricultural produce, but
there are also important plastic, metal and manufacturing as well as electronic
industries. Shipping know-how has long-standing traditions.
The province also has an Institute of Higher Education and a Police College

Sailboats at Eckerö,
Åland.

Jomala church is one of Åland's
most popular tourist attractions.

Åland is a demilitarized autonomous province belonging to Finland. It consists of 16 municipalities. It is a beautiful island with 6500 islets and skerries. The official language of Åland is Swedish.

The Province of Åland

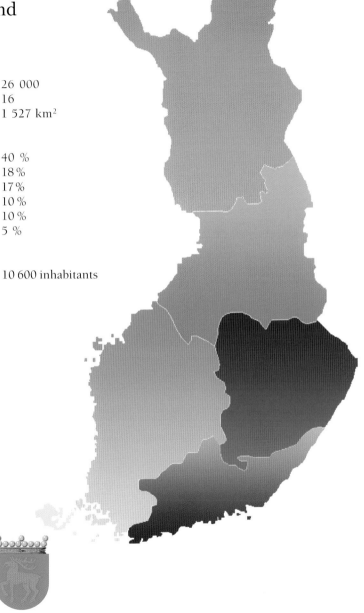

Number of inhabitants	26 000
Municipalities	16
Land surface area	1 527 km^2

Business structure	
Services and tourism	40 %
Traffic and navigation	18 %
Trade and banking	17 %
Industry	10 %
Agriculture and forestry	10 %
Building industry	5 %

City	
Mariehamn	10 600 inhabitants

Biggest business enterprises
Viking Line
Eckerö Line
Chips
Optinova

Summer twilight in Helsinki. >

House of Parliament, Helsinki.

Turku Castle is one of the most famous tourist attractions in Western Finland.
Its foundations date as far back as the 13th century.

Finlandiahouse, Helsinki.

Know-how in Southern Finland

The county of Southern Finland is Finland's biggest growth area. Helsinki, Espoo and Vantaa constitute the suburban area of Helsinki, housing nearly one third of the country's total population. Information technology, communication, electronics, tourism and services are among the most important fields of know-how in Southern Finland. The cooperation between the University of Helsinki, Helsinki Technical University and the Espoo-Vantaa Polytechnic provides the necessary resources for state-of-the-art innovations and know-how.

Business and administration are concentrated to Helsinki, whereas Espoo is the know-how centre of the electronics industry, communication, space technology and low temperature physics. The airport city Vantaa is an air traffic junction and logistics centre, offering an ideal location and growth environment for national and international enterprises.

Halikko near the city of Salo in the country of Finland Proper. Geenhouses in a rural setting.

Finland's most important centres of administration, business, traffic and communication are situated in the County of Southern Finland, and 40 % of the total amount of work places is concentrated to this region. The county consists of six provinces; Kanta Häme, Päijät-Häme, Uusimaa, Eastern Uusimaa, Kymen-laakso and South Karelia. The county also has vast culture landscapes and a genuine countryside.

County of Southern Finland

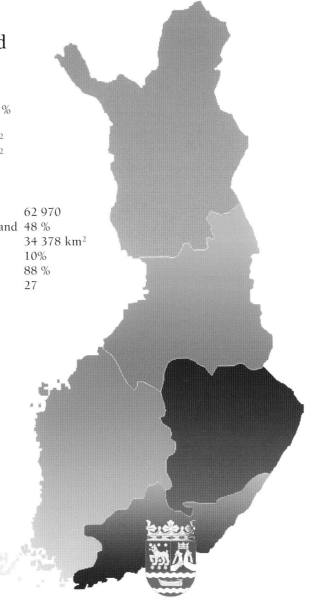

Population   2 106 717- %
of Finland's total population   40 %
Population density   70 inh./km^2
- the whole country   17 inh./km^2
Swedish speaking population 138 031
-% of Swedish speaking population
in the whole country   48 %
Foreigners   62 970
- % of total amount of foreigners in Finland 48 %
Surface area   34 378 km^2
of Finland's total surface area   10%
Municipalities   88 %
-of which number of cities   27

Business structure
Services   73 %
Industry   23,2 %
Agriculture and forestry   2,0 %
Other   1,4 %
(Central Statistical Office)

Biggest business enterprises
Nokia
Stora Enso
Nordea Bank Finland
Fortum
UPM-Kymmene
Metsäliitto
Kesko
Outokumpu
Metso
Kone

Biggest cities and nr. of inhabitants
Helsinki 559330 ,Espoo 224231,
Vantaa 184039, Lahti 98253,
Kotka 54618, Hämeenlinna 46909,
Porvoo 46217, Hyvinkää 43169,
Järvenpää 36602, Lohja 35647.

Interior view of the Helsinki University Library.

University of Helsinki – A Leading European University

Of all institutions of higher education in Finland, the University of Helsinki has the widest range of disciplines. It was established in Turku in 1640, but was transferred to Helsinki in 1828. Currently the number of faculties is nine, but from the beginning of 2004 it will increase to eleven. There are 38 000 degree students and 7 300 staff. The number of degrees taken each year is 4 200, of which 350 are doctorates.

The university concentrates on high-level scientific research and researcher education. Scientific research is also the basis of the teaching provided by the University, the operations of which support the development of society as well as business and industry. University representatives offer their competencies for the benefit of society through a number of positions of trust and expertise.

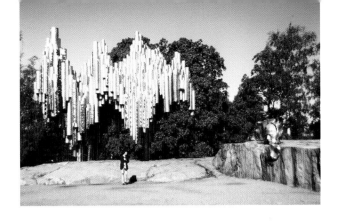

The impressive Sibelius-monument by professor Eila Hiltunen was finished in 1967. It is one of Helsinki's most popular tourist attractions.

Temppeliaukio church and the Sibelius monument are the most famous tourist attractions in Helsinki.

Temppeliaukio church, designed by architects Timo and Tuomo Suomalainen was finished in 1969. The church is built in a rock and surrounded by a solid stone wall. Under the beautiful cupola made of copper and glass there are seats for 740 persons. The church is also known for its outstanding acoustics.

The main building of the University of Helsinki is designed by C.L.Engel. >

N E T L A N D E R

Antares–Finland's National Space Research Programme

The space research programme Antares focuses on space science and environmental remote sensing. The programme will be carried out in 2001-2004, consisting of extensive projects established by consortia of space research institutes. The programme is international, and many of its projects are related to the programmes of the European Space Agency (ESA), including "Planck -Cosmic Microwave Background", " Integral – Black Holes" and "Mars Express – Study of the Planet Mars". Antares is funded by Tekes and the Academy of Finland.

The Antares space research programme addresses the Finnish space strategy on a practical level. The essential areas of the strategy are scientific and technological research based on satellite observations, satellite remote sensing, telecommunication and navigation. Common features in these areas are instrument and sensor building, development of observational and analytical methods. Up to 25 Finnish space instruments on board satellites are utilized in the programme. The Antares programme focuses on space science and scientific environmental remote sensing. The objective is to achieve measurable results in Finnish space research and boost it to the highest possible level.

"ENVISAT" is an advanced polar-orbiting Earth Observation Satellite which will provide measurements of the atmosphere, ocean and ice over a five-year period. Project "Antares project "ASSIMENVI".

JEM-X on board Integral spacecraft launched on 17 October 2002 to study how gravitational energy release as matter falls into super massive black holes. The study will be made by the Finnish gamma-ray detector. Project "ESA".

The French-Finnish Netlander mission to the planet Mars will be launched in 2009 to study the Martian environment. Project: "DAPSS".

Väinö Kelhä, Research Professor in space technology of the Technical Research Centre of Finland.

Academy professor Matti Krusius carrying out helium research with a rotating cryostate inside a protected chamber.

Expertise in Low Temperature Technology at the Technical University of Helsinki

This Magnetoencephalographic (MEG) installation (picture) is situated in a magnetically shielded room at the brain research department of the low-temperature laboratory of the Technical University of Helsinki.. The instrument is manufactured by Neuromag Oy. The 306 devices measuring the magnetic fields are surrounded by liquid helium at a temperature of 4 Kelvin (-269 o C). The extremely sensitive measuring instrument can measure the magnetic fields generated by neural electric activity and register brain reactions in time and space.

The Helsinki Technical University in Espoo, Otaniemi, was built in 1964. It is designed by Alvar Aalto.>

Energy from the Sun

Naps Systems Oy, located in Vantaa, supplies high quality decentralized power systems based on photovoltaic technology. Naps'solutions range from smaller standardised to larger custom-designed systems. Naps systems are powering telecommunication stations, buildings, navigation equipment, water pumping, summer cottages, schools and health centres as well as many other locations and applications worldwide. During its history, Naps Systems has supplied over 200 000 systems to 50 countries.

The system for Finland's first solar powered apartment building, located in the Viikki area in Helsinki is one of the many systems supplied by Naps. The solar panels are integrated as balcony balustrades. The efficiency of the solar panels is 24 kW, which corresponds to 15-20 % of the total electricity requirement in a building with 39 apartments. During the summer months, surplus solar electricity is fed into the public grid, and in winter it is redistributed to the building by the local electricity company.

Nokia is the world´s leading mobile phone supplier and a
leading supplier of fixed telecom networks.

A leader in cordless solutions, Nokia aims at improving corporate efficiency and enhancing
people´s every-day life by combining the advantages of cordless systems with the internet.

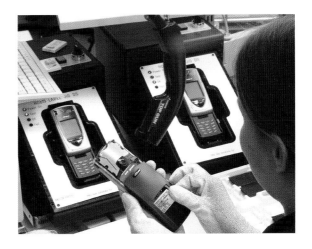

Nokia headquarters at Keilaniemi in the
city of Espoo is designed by Pekka Helin.>

Heureka's outdoor exhibition, science Park Galilei, is open during the summer months.
The ancient Archimedes Screw is still used to raise water.

Different idioms emerge from the language globe.

Heureka! – The Joy of Discovery is Everyman's right

Heureca, located in Vantaa, 15 km outside Helsinki, is Finland's largest science centre and an interactive exhibition centre for the whole family. Heureka aims at offering its visitors the joy of discovery and inspiration through science-related exhibits and programmes. The visitor plays an active part, doing and trying all kinds of interesting things, offering a great opportunity for children to get acquainted with the world of science and technology. The main exhibition consists of the Minerva science theatre, the Children's laboratory, Open Laboratory and a special area for small children. There are also temporary exhibitions and an outdoor exhibition in the Galilei Science Park which is open during the summer months.

Exhibition languages are Finnish, Swedish and English. Exhibits created by Heureka are exported all over the world. Millions of people in different countries have seen the exhibits called "Illusion", "Communication", "Ancient Cultures" and "Forest". Many Finnish researchers and innovative companies support Heureka's exhibit production. The jewel of Heureka is the Jules Verne Theatre. It is Finland's biggest planetarium. The films shown in this three-dimensional space give the audience a spectacular insight in the wonders of nature. Heureka also offers ideal facilities for meetings and festivities.

The blue and white Finnair Airbus A 320 in its right element above the clouds.

The Helsinki-Vantaa Airport – One of the Best in the World

In an international comparison in 1999, Helsinki-Vantaa airport was elected the best airport in the world, and it still maintains a top position in international comparisons. The airport is clean and well planned with excellent services. The international and domestic terminals are situated at walking distance. The airport, within 30 minutes' drive from Helsinki is used by about 10 million travellers every year.

View from the Meripuisto Park in Helsinki.>

Rubber Tyred Gantry Cranes from Konecranes – Modern and Reliable

Continuous repeat orders confirm the technology leadership of Konecranes Rubber Tyred Gantry Cranes (RTG). Since introduction of the new design it has been a clear leader.
All its features are electromechanical, with no hydraulic involved.
KCI Konecranes own AC Frequency Control System composes the most modern and reliable drive for RTG´s. Eliminating the hydraulic systems and utilizing AC drives significantly reduces the maintenance costs of the RTG´s.

The huge glass wall in the Forest hall of the Sibelius hall offers a breathtaking view over lake Vesi-järvi.

The Sibelius-hall – Finnish Architecture and Wood Construction Technology

The Sibelius-hall, a wooden congress- and concert hall in the city of Lahti, is the only concert and congress centre in the world constructed out of wood. It is designed by Finnish architects Hannu Tikka and Kimmo Lintula. The building consists of four parts: the old carpenter's study, the Forest hall, the main hall and the congress wing. The outstanding acoustic system in the main wing is designed by Russell Johnson, Artec Consultants Inc., New York. The auditorium and galleries are built in oval shape in the so called Shoe-box Hall. Acoustics are adjustable in the echo chambers on both sides of the main hall through 188 wall baffles that open and close. 2,7 km of woollen fabric has been used for the curtains in the main hall.

Acoustic baffles open on the echo chambers on both sides of the main hall.

Know-how in Western Finland

The county of Western Finland is known for its ship building technology and metal industry.
The Turku Science Park promotes know-how and generates new business activities, for example in information and communication technology and biotechnology. The University of Jyväskylä offers necessary resources for the development of knowledge in enterprises and institutions. The Tampere area is known for its industry, health care technology and information technology. Aker Finnyards in Rauma is a world leading ferry builder, and Valmet Automotive in the city of Uusikaupunki assembles Porsche cars.

< Tall ships Race in Turku lures enthusiasts to the shores of Aurajoki river.

One third of Finland's total population lives in the county of Western Finland. The county consists of seven provinces, i.e. Finland Proper, Satakunta, Pirkanmaa, Central Finland, South Ostrobothnia, Ostrobothnia and Central Ostrobothnia. Major industries are shipbuilding, metal industry and biotechnology.

County of Western Finland

Population	1 843 225
Population density	24,8 inh./km²
Municipalities	204
Surface area	74 185 km²

Business structure	
Primary production	5,8 %
Processing industry	31,0 %
Service	61,2 %
Other	2,0 %

Education	
Graduated	58,0 %
Intermediate education graduates	37,02 %
Higher education graduates	21,9 %

Biggest cities	Nr. of inhabitants
Tampere	200966
Turku	175059
Jyväskylä	82409
Pori	76189
Vaasa	56953
Rauma	37034
Kokkola	35583
Jyväskylä	33485
Seinäjoki	31085
Nokia	27635

Biggest business enterprises
HK Ruokatalo Oyj, Keskimaa Osk,
 Nokian Renkaat Oyj, Outokumpu
Poricopper Oy,
Pilkington Automotive Finland Oy,
 Ruokamarkkinat Oy, Sandvik Tamrock Oy,
Tamfelt Oyj Abb, Valmet Automotive Oy,
Valtra Oy Ab, Wärtsilä-Finland Oy

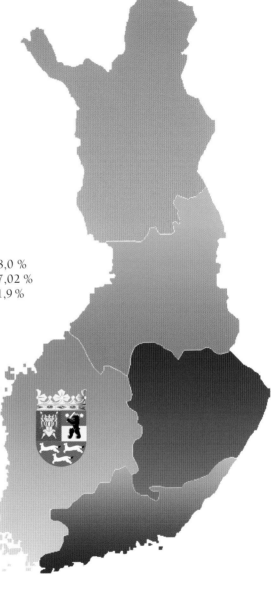

Marine Power Generation

Wärtsilä Corporation is the leading global ship power supplier and a major provider of solutions for decentralized power generation and supporting services. Wärtsilä Corporation is the leading global ship power supplier and a major provider of solutions for decentralized power generation and supporting services.Wärtsilä also operates a Nordic Engineering steel company, Imatra Steel. The company's power divisions provide complete solutions for power generation and marine propulsion systems. Wärtsilä designs, manufactures, licenses, sells and maintains 500-80.000 kW WÄRTSI-LÄ and SULZER motors and their applications, using heavy and light fuel oils or gas. Wärtsilä's power plant products are based on environmentally advanced equipment that offers new solutions for renewable energy.

Korsnäs Wind Farm near the City of Vaasa

ABB Finland, located in Vaasa, has developed synchronous motors and generators based on permanent magnet technology suitable for applications ranging from paper machines and marine propulsion systems to wind turbines.

M/S Romantika built for Tallink is the first totally new vessel in ten years on the Gulf of Finland. It is also the biggest cruise ferry in Estonia to date. The 192, 90 m long and 29 m in beam vessel sailing on the Helsinki-Tallinn route has capacity for 2,500 passengers. The interiors of cruise liner standard have been created by four specialist architects, each focusing on different aspects of the onterior layout.

Innovative Shipbuilding

Aker Finnyards, based in Rauma, is the leading ferry builder in the world. Its main business areas are ferries, cruise vessels, naval craft and multipurpose icebreakers. Deliveries in the last three years include the world's largest cruise ferry for Ireland, the fastest ferry in the English Channel for France, Estonia's biggest cruise ferry, as well as three passenger ferries for Scotland.

Already in earlier days, definitions such as "The largest" and "The first in the world" have been used for the vessels designed and built in Rauma , as the 1500 ships built include ships such as the first multipurpose icebreakers and the world's biggest aluminium catamarans. During the last few years, Aker Finnyards has been focusing on advancing the working processes and multiplying the number of subcontractors. Simultaneously, the yard's concept, having traditionally been quite production oriented, is now strictly market oriented, starting from
the evaluation of our clients' needs.

Both of the Finnish shipyardsAker Finnyards and Kvaerner Masa-Yards are part of the Aker Kvaerner Yards group of shipyards, employing 16 000 people in 14 yards worldwide, with a turnover of 2,5 billion euro. The combined shipbuilding operations of Aker Kvaerner Yards rank number one among European shipyard groups in terms of revenues, and number four worldwide.

Building special ships requires continuous development, investments and R&D, but also constant employee training. As a proof of success in this Aker Finnyards received the ISO 9001 quality certification in 1998 covering all activities of both 800 blue-collar and 200 white-collar employees.

A Finnish Success Story –
Design Pertti Palmroth / Hamken Oy

In 1952, Pentti Palmroth returned to Finland after having completed his studies at Northampton Technical College in England and Technische Fachschule in Germany. He started working at the shoe factory in Tampere, founded by his father in 1928. Shortly thereafter he launched his first design collection of ladies'shoes and boots.

From the very beginning, footwear designed by Pertti Palmroth have been known for their clear design concept, original styling and high quality. The popularity of his collection increased rapidly, and soon Pertti Palmroth started marketing his line of ladies' footwear abroad. The first export country in 1958 was Sweden, where Pertti Palmroth's designs were considered original and fashionable.

After the introduction in the Nordic countries, the collection was successfully introduced in well-known shops and department stores in USA, Canada, the Netherlands, Germany, Austria, etc. International fashion magazines like Vogue, Elle, Harper's Bazaar and Burda featured Pertti Palmrooth's line of ladies' footwear in their most exclusive fashion photos. In the mid-1980s Pertti Palmroth developed a new synthetic footwear material designed to resist difficult, changing weather conditions. This material, developed for "every kind of weather" has many characteristics that are superior to leather. The material is resistant to rain, snow and cold weather, keeping in excellent condition without special protection, and still maintains its permeability

The new material soon reached the same popularity as original leather, and now accounts for about 70 % of the factory's entire production. Footwear manufactured of this new material has gained vast international popularity, and is now sold in prestigious shops and department stores all over the world. In the mid-1980s, simultaneously with the introduction of the new material , Pertti Palmroth founded an own business chain.

The first shops were opened in Finland. Presently Pertti Palmroth-shops have been established also in Sweden, Norway, the Netherlands and Germany. The Pertti Palmroth brand of footwear is manufactured in Tampere, Pirkkala and Virrat. The average daily production is about 700 pairs, and some 70 % of the production is exported. The staff at the Pertti Palmroth factories and shops presently amounts to 250 employees.

Bio Valley comprises 26 hectares in Turku Science Park with a construction right of over 110.000m

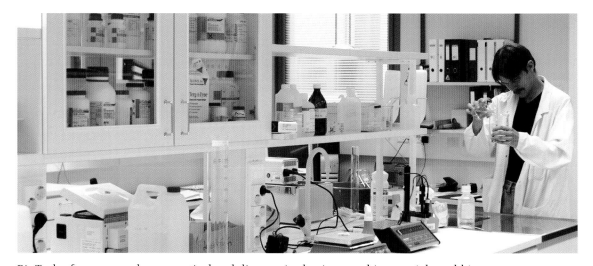

BioTurku focuses on pharmaceutical and diagnostics businesses, biomaterials and bioprocesses, as well as functional foods.

The BioTurku Chain Promotes Health

The majority of Finnish biotech research and development takes place in the Turku region on the South-West coast of Finland. BioTurku is a community of all biotech actors in the Turku region. The BioTurku concept refers to a chain stretching from training and research to bioscience entrepreneurship and production. The main activities are located at the Turku Science Park, stretching from the universities to Turku Bio Valley.

The main building of the University of Jyväskylä, which was completed in 1955, and the surrounding campus with its architectural treasures from different time periods are based on Alvar Aalto's designs.

University of Jyväskylä – a Campus of Excellence and Architectural Treasures

Nano Science Centre gathers researchers in physics, chemistry and biology together around its core - a shared laboratory, professors Päivi Törmä and Jorma Virtanen explain.

The main campus of the University of Jyväskylä has been built on the basis of Alvar Aalto's designs. Over 15 000 students, as well as exchange students from 150 universities, study in the University's seven faculties. Research cooperation is practised with scholars from nearly a thousand universities. The University of Jyväskylä, established in 1934 as Jyväskylä College of Education, continues the rapid growth which started in the 1990s.

The University of Jyväskylä has five national Centres of Excellence in Research. The first three study human development and its risk factors, evolutionary ecology and nuclear and material physics.The centre studying the history of mind, as well as the one focusing on geometric and mathematical physics are joint ventures with the University of Helsinki.
The University of Jyväskylä has a special status for its high-quality adult education and two other nationally recognized high-quality teaching units. Its faculty for Sports and Health Sciences is the only one of its kind in Finland. The university is also known for its active role in developing innovations in education and research, especially in collaboration with business and commerce as well as with other actors of the region.

Tampere city centre: Pine trees the Pyynikki ridge (front), Näsinneula Opservation Tower and lake Näsijärvi in the background.>

Olavinlinna castle in the city of Savonlinna is internationally renowned for its splendid opera summer festivals.

Know-how in Eastern Finland

Wood industry is an obvious know-how area in Eastern Finland. Pharmaceutics, health care technology and environmental technology are among the specialities of the area around the city of Kuopio. Cooperation between the university, the polytechnic and the business enterprises have generated innovations, of which one is the combination of wood and plastic. This has enabled manufacture and export of many kinds of useful household articles.
The city of Savonlinna has gained a world reputation as a meeting point for cultural know-how.

Laura Pyrrö,
winner of the Timo Mustakallio song contest 2002.

< View from the County of Eastern Finland; Hovinmäki at Rääkkylä.

The county of Eastern Finland comprises 81 % of Finland's forest area and 35,7 % of its total lake area. The county consists of three provinces; South Savo, North Savo and Northern Karelia. The shared borderline with Russia is 296 km.

County of Eastern Finland

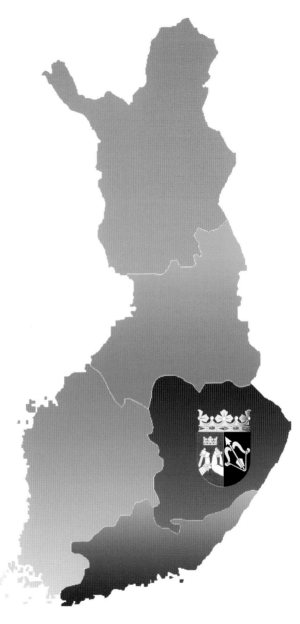

Number of inhabitants	584 974
Municipalities	66
Land area	48 727 km²
Water area	11 992 km²

Business structure
Primary production	9,2 %
Processing industry	24 %
Services	64 %

Education
Graduated	57,6 %
Intermediate education graduates	38,3 %
Higher education graduates	19,3 %

Biggest cities / Inhabitants
Kuopio	88250
Joensuu	52659
Mikkeli	46511
Savonlinna	27602
Varkaus	22938
Iisalmi	22835
Nurmes	9430
Outokumpu	7995
Suonenjoki	7886
Juva	7449

Biggest business enterpris
Stora Enso Oyj, Varkaus mill
Foster Wheeler Energy Plc, Varkaus
Kemira Phosphates Oy, Siilinjärvi
Atria Oyj, Kuopio
Tamfelt Oyj, Juankoski
Fenestra Oy, Kuopio
Ponsse Oyj, Vieremä
Honeywell Oy, Varkaus
M-Real Savon Sellu, Kuopio
Schauman Woods, Kuopio mill

Mikkeli Polytechnic educates young top experts in many fields

The Finnish higher education system comprises two parallel sectors that complement each other: universities and polytechnics. The universities emphasize scientific research, whereas polytechnics are institutes of high-level post-secondary education with a more practical approach. Mikkeli Polytechnic is one of Finland's 29 polytechnics. In Mikkeli there are twenty different degree programmes and three of which are in English. Information technology and other branches of technology are among the main subjects.

Mikkeli Polytechnic's International Summer Term, the largest event of its kind in Finland, brings exchange students from partner institutions from other countries to Mikkeli every year.

At Mikkeli Polytechnic students are offered many interesting study programmes.

Stone is a fascinating material

The activities of the Finnish Stone Centre are concentrated around a single substance: natural stone. The centre is networking natural-stone related research, training and product development organizations at a national and international level. The Centre participates in testing and norm setting and distributes relevant information to industry and designers in its field of activity.
Furthermore, the centre helps in establishing and developing handicraft and entrepreneur activities on the domestic market and business activities for the export markets.

Turo Tailor — More than 60 years at the Service of Well Dressed Gentlemen

Turo Oy was established in 1938 in the city of Kuopio. In the beginning, the company manufactured mostly working clothes, uniforms and sportswear. In the early 1960s Turo started industrial confection of men's wear, and around 1980 they decided to concentrate solely on the confection of men's suits. In 1988 the name was changed to Oy Turo Tailor Ab. Today, Turo Tailor is the biggest manufacturer of men's suits in the Nordic Countries, producing about 600 suits every day. Main market areas, besides the domestic market, are Sweden, Norway and Denmark. In the year 2000 Turo Tailor received the prestigious Golden Hanger award for outstanding design and quality.

Sauna and Finland

Sauna and "sisu" (the typically Finnish type of stamina) are important parts of the Finnish identity. Saunasystems, manufactured by Oy SaunaMare Ltd , located in Kuopio, takes the Finnish sauna tradition into a new era. Saunasystems is a Finnish high-tech sauna heating system equipped with ventilation and humidity systems.

Natural Fibre Composites – Wood Industry Knowhow in Karelia

During the last decades many sectors of the wood industry have seen a significant increase in market shares for plastic products. In several European countries the use of PVC-windows has increased, although traditional wooden window frames are still holding a leading position. A new challenge is to combine plastic and wood technology. Composite products offer new possibilities for the use of wood, and have a significant importance for wood consumption, as more than 50% of composite products can consist of wood fibre.

Natural fibre composites complement, diversify and extend the field of application of Scandinavian wood species. Natural fibre composites can be classified as new "green" materials, combining the strength of natural fibres with the resistance to humidity, wear and tear and microbes typical to durable plastic materials. The material can be processed directly into the final product without waste. No poisonous raw materials are used in the production, making the end products suitable for recycling, either crushed, reprocessed or burned to energy without harmful pollution.

Natural fibre composites are especially suitable for the production of complex forms that are recyclable, and they are also expected to be suitable for replacing special plastics, PVC, and aluminium and decay-resistant rain forest timber.

The development of natural fibre technology was started in 2000 by the Wood Technology Centre Puugia administered by the Joensuu Science Park in cooperation with the Chemistry Department of Joensuu University. Today, 20 Finnish companies participate in the project, the objective of which is to develop production technology and tailor-made end products to the companies participating in the project. A number of products are already in production. The composite material is manufactured by Kareline Oy Ltd.

This injection-moulded electric guitar is a good example of the excellent audio-technical properties of the natural fibre composite material and its adaptability to tailor-made solutions. The guitar is manufactured by Flaxwood Ltd.

Household goods made from composite materials are hygienic and safe. They can be machine-washed and safely burned at the end of their life-cycle. Cups and glasses known under the brand-name of Kupilka are manufactured by Joensuun Meskari Oy.

In a round window, the stability and exact reproductibility of the natural fibre composite material guarantee optimum moulding characteristics.

Koli is the highest mountain in Eastern Finland. It rises 235 metres above the surface of Lake Pielisjärvi.>
Young snow-boarders in North Karelia. >

Know-how in the County of Oulu

The county of Oulu is a rapidly developing growth centre. The university and polytechnic provide possibilities for know-how development in the enterprises of the region. Oulu Technopolis Oyj is Finland's biggest company specialized in the field of business environments for technology companies, with a service concept combining modern office facilities, services to companies and individuals as well as corporate development services and programmes. Information technology, metal industry and services are other areas of knowledge in the County of Oulu.

Industry and services are the main sources of outcome in the county of Oulu. The business strategy of Northern Finland, the multipolis-network and other programmes developed by the Oulu region Centre of Expertise create possibilities for new ventures and employment.

The County of Oulu

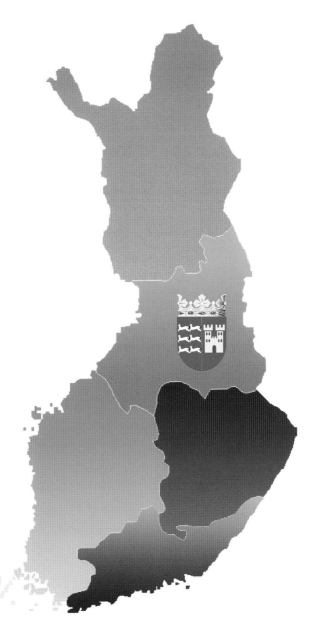

Number of inhabitants	457 345
Population density	8 inh./km^2
Municipalities	50
Surface area	57 000 km^2

Education
Graduated	60,7 %
Intermediate education graduates	36,5 %
Higher education graduates	23,7 %

Biggest cities /Inhabitants
Oulu	125928
Kajaani	35842
Raahe	22822
Kuusamo	17580
Ylivieska	13220
Kuhmo	10787

Business structure
Primary production	6,7 %
Industry	27,5%
Services	63,1%

Biggest Enterprises and Establishments
Rautaruukki Steel, Nokia,
Stora-Enso, UPM Kymmene,
Kesko, NK Cables,
Arina, Scanfi, Elektrobit,
ADR Haanpää, PKK Group,
Filtronic LK,Polar Electro,
Wettri, Pörhön autoliike,
Osuuskauppa Maakunta, Oulu University,
VTT Technical Research Centre of Finland,
Medipolis, Technopolis Oulu and
Kajaani Technology Park.

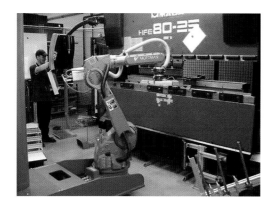

Elektrometalli Oy – Finnish Know-how in the Oulu region

Elektrometalli Oy at Kempele, Oulu ,was established in 1975, and it specializes in a fairly narrow sector; the manufacture of thin plates. This specialization enables the company to serve their clients in the best possible way, providing optimal services and high-quality products. One of Elektrometalli Oy's most important growth areas is the rapidly expanding electronics and telecommunications sector which is constantly requiring new solutions and applications in the field of thin plate technology.

Product development and manufacture of existing and new products is carried out in close cooperation with the clients. The company's entire arsenal of skills and know-how are at the clients' disposal.

Continuing development is one of the company's main challenges. Every year considerable investments are made in production technology, product development and training.
As this industry needs specialized knowledge and skills, nearly every employee receives in-house training. The quality of the work is guaranteed by a quality system according to ISO-9002 standards. The company's whole personnel are dedicated to continuous quality.

Elektrometalli Oy designs and manufactures different thin plate components for the electronics, fibre optics and communication industries, using design systems such as Vertex 3-D and Autocad programmes, which enable tailor-made solutions according to the clients' needs.

Oulu, city library and theatre house.

Oulu, Meritulli visitors marina and the theatre.

Measurepolis – Kajaani

Measurepolis-Kajaani offers measurement technology with signal processing in the main wood processing industry, developed by the Measurement and Sensor Laboratory of Oulu University's Kajaani Research and Development Centre. The research unit has developed and strengthened its know-how in measurement technology since the beginning of the 1990s. Kajaani Polytechnic has contributed to the activity by training experts in measurement technology for the needs of hi-tech companies. Today, Kajaani is internationally known for its outstanding research, training, development, as well as its efficient measurement technology companies.

Since the beginning of 2003, Measurepolis-Kajaani has been responsible for measurement technology in the national Centre of Expertise Programme. Measurepolis-Kajaani consists of companies in the field of measurement technology, Kajaani Technology Centre, the Measurement and Sensor Laboratory of Oulu University, Kajaani Polytechnic, VTT Technical Research Centre of Finland and Snowpolis-Vuokatti. The core know-how of the centre consists of optical measurement techniques, embedded systems, electronic testing and wireless instrumentation.

Technopolis – An Ideal Environment for High Tech Companies

Technopolis Oulu Plc is a high-tech real estate and service group operating in Oulu, Finland. It is the biggest technology park in Finland, with 8000 employees and about 600 companies. It organises the building of business premises, and hires these to high tech enterprises in Oulu Technology Park. The concept, developed over more than 20 years, consists of modern business premises and versatile business development services to high tech companies. Technopolis has real estate and service units at Linnanmaa University Campus (picture), in Kontinkangas and in Kempele. Plans are in progress to build a new unit in the Oulu city centre.

Lake Oulujärvi >>

Know-how in Lapland

Tourism is one of the main sources of livelihood in the County of Lapland. Future top experts in different fields graduate from the university and polytechnic. A rapid development can be seen in the industry and business sectors. Lapland also has an important brewing industry. Souvenirs manufactured by the Sámi population are masterpieces of an ancient handicraft tradition. The Sámi people have lived of reindeer herding during many generations, but today, many Sámis are active in science and research.

The county of Lapland is situated within the North Calotte and the Barents Sea region, bordering on Russia in the East, Norway in the North and Sweden in the West. It is Finland's largest, albeit most sparsely populated county, comprising 29 % of the country's total surface area.

The County of Lapland

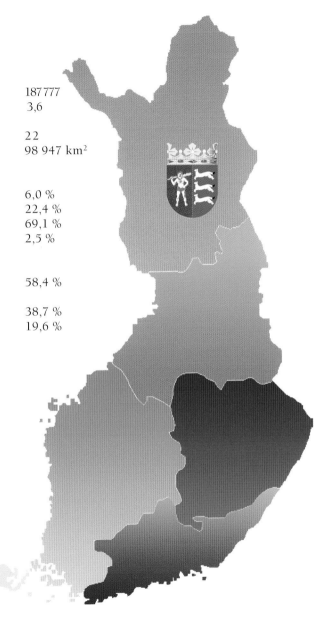

Number of inhabitants	187 777
% of Finland's total number of inhabitants	3,6
Population density/ 2 inhabitants/km²	
Municipalities	22
Surface area	98 947 km²

Business Structure	
Primary production	6,0 %
Processing industry	22,4 %
Services and tourism	69,1 %
Other	2,5 %

Education	
Graduated	58,4 %
Intermediate education graduates	38,7 %
Higher education graduates	19,6 %

Biggest cities / Number of inhabitants
Rovaniemi	35110
Kemi	23236
Tornio	22155
Kemijärvi	9936

Biggest business enterprises
Kemijoki Veitsiluodon tehtaat
Stora Enso
Avesta Polarit
Metsäliitto
Hartwall Oy Kemi
Lapin Kulta
Kemijoki-Yhtiö
Bombardier Nordtrac Oy
Lappset Group Oy
VR

Joulupukki TV Ltd

Joulupukki TV Ltd is a company established in 2000, employing five persons and a number of sub-suppliers. The company is based in Rovaniemi at the Polar Circle, and produces digital Christmas and tourism-related material for television, internet and mobile phones. The company also offers consulting services for the leisure industry. Clients are mainly from Finland, France and other European countries.

The product range of Joulupukki TV includes Santa's internet television channel, (www.santatv.com) Santas DVD and background colour imagery for mobile phones. Joulupukki TV Ltd has developed its expertise in international amusement park and museum activities. A digital play-pavilion coordinated by Joulupukki TV was inaugurated in 2003 in the French Futuroscope Amusement Park in Poitiers near Paris.

Arktikum – the Arctic Centre

In the centre of Rovaniemi on the shore of the Ounasjoki river rises an extraordinary architectonic sight, the Arktikum science centre (the Arctic Centre) and a museum (the Provincial Museum of Lapland). The museum focuses on Nordic and Arctic regions and presents the life, habitats, history, customs and culture of the peoples living north of the Arctic Circle. The building also comprises a cinema, restaurant, science shop, as well as a meeting and conference centre. The Arktikum building is designed by Danish architects Biech-Bonderup & Throup-Waade.

Lake Kilpisjärvi >
Pallastunturi >>

Earlier publications
by Raimo Suikkari

Sininen rakkaus, poems, 1992

Suomen luontokuvia/Pictures of Nature in Finland, 1992

Sininen unelma, poems, 1993

Suomea Helsingistä Lappiin/Finland from Helsinki to Lapland, 1993

Vihreän planeetan kutsu, scifi, 1993

Helsinki-book, 1994

Sininen uni, poems, 1995

Finland 2000, 1996

Ystäväsi Suomi/Your Friend Finland, 1997

Sininen hiljaisuus, poems, 1997

Suomen kaunis Lappi/Beautiful Finnish Lapland, 1997

Helsinki Espoo ja Vantaa-book, 1998

Finland today, 1999

Runokuvia Suomen Lapista/Poetic Images of Finnish Lapland, 1999

Tammen laulu/The Song of the Oak trees, multivideo, 2000

Nähtävyyksien Suomi/Sights in Finland, 2000

Enkelihiutaleita, poems, 2000

Helsinki Sights and Attractions, 2001

Suomi vuodenaikojen sinfonia/Finland A Symphony of Seasons, 2001

Nuuksion laulu/The Song of Nuuksio, 2002

Hetken tanssi, poems, 2002

Litorinameren poika, juvenile book, 2003

EUROPEAN DESTINATIONS

Lakselv · Murmansk

Artic Circle

Rovaniemi

Bergen
Oslo
Turku · Helsinki · St. Petersburg
Stockholm · Tallinn
Gothenburg · Riga · Moscow
Copenhagen · Vilnius
Dublin
Manchester
Hamburg
Amsterdam · Berlin · Warsaw
London
Düsseldorf
Brussels
Frankfurt · Prague
Paris
Munich · Vienna
Zürich · Budapest
Milan · Verona
Nice · Rimini
Madrid
Barcelona · Istanbul
Rome
Faro · Naples · Thessaloniki
Malaga
Athens
Rhodes
Chania · Heraklion

☐ Seasonal service   ■ Scheduled destinations   ■ Leisure destinations

FINNAIR